"...a gay couple whose alternatively sweet and cantankerous relationship rings with the truth of genuine love between two people, regardless of gender or gender preference."
— *Robert Danté, The Boudoir Noir*

"New Yorker humour for a gay and lesbian readership"
— *Alberta Gay and Lesbian Press*

"...a campy cartoon that has tackled topics as frivolous as shopping, as relevant as commitment, and as important (and rarely spoken of) as gay domestic abuse."
— *au courant*

"...rarely political but, rather, 'thinkable'..."
— *GO Info*

"Without resorting to cheap shots or insensitive slurs, Sean uncovers the humour in our lives and our lifestyles. It's the sort of thing that makes you wince and laugh at the same time."
— *Joseph Bean, Drummer*

"NB to readers: Martin's pretty cute."
— *Malebox*

SEAN MARTIN

CAUGHT ON TAPE

AN ANTHOLOGY OF
DOC & RAIDER CARTOONS

To g/g –
Gay day '95 –
ooo baby –
Sean Martin

A HIGHLY QUESTIONABLE BOOK
FROM
QUEER PRESS

Canadian Cataloguing in Publication Data

Martin, Sean, 1955 -
Doc & Raider: Caught on Tape

ISBN 1-895564-03-4

1. Gay male couples - Caricatures and cartoons
2. Homosexuality - Caricatures and cartoons
3. Canadian wit and humour, Pictorial. I. Title.

NC 1449.M37A4 1994   741.5 ' 971   C94-932328-4

All characters and events portrayed in this book are fictitious, and any
resemblance to any person living or dead (unless mentioned with satirical
intent) is purely coincidental... honest. I mean it.
No, really, I do.

Book design by Sean Martin
Production services provided by The Zoom Room, Toronto

Published by
Queer Press NonProfit Community Publishing of Toronto
PO Box 485, Station P, Toronto, Ontario M5S 2T1

First edition, published October, 1994

Printed in Canada

I wonder if the networks would be interested if they knew *we* were based on a shockingly true story...

With a great big hug,
to John & Paul and Steve & Tian
who never really knew how much
they inspired this nonsense

and

to Steven J.,
now gone, but the one
who will always be my Doc

Doc and Raider, those mad gadabouts, have appeared in the following publications *(partial listing)*: *Xtra!* (Toronto, ON), *Angles* (Vancouver, BC), *Rites* (Toronto, ON), *GO Info* (Ottawa, ON), *Capital Xtra!* (Ottawa, ON), *Perceptions* (Saskatoon, SK), *AGLP* (Calgary, AB), *Gaezette* (Halifax, NS), *CLUE* (Calgary, AB), *Bullsheets* (Portland, OR), *Boots* (Toronto, ON), *Out!* (Auckland, NZ), *Gay Scotland* (Edinburgh), *Drummer* (San Francisco, CA), *The Bridge* (Salt Lake City, UT), *Out* (Pittsburgh, PA), *Twist Weekly* (Seattle, WA), *Lexicon* (Toronto, ON), *Blikk* (Oslo, NO), *Reporter* (Stockholm, SW), *The Leather Journal* (San Francisco, CA), *The International Gay Men's News* (Merrifield, VA), *Gay Comix* (Portland, OR), the *Meatmen* Collections (San Francisco, CA), and *A Queer Sense of Humour* (Toronto, ON), as well as newsletters and other ephemera for the AIDS Committee of Ottawa, the Vancouver Persons With AIDS Society, Gathering of the Clans III (Winnipeg, MB), Vancouver Activists in S/M, the Pacific Northwest Wrestling Club (Vancouver, BC), Bushwack Theatre (Toronto, ON), the International Mr. Drummer Competition (San Francisco, CA), Forge Studios (Toronto, ON), Making Scenes (Ottawa, ON), Village Clinic (Winnipeg, MB), Big City Hoedown II and III (Toronto, ON), Team Toronto, Casey House (Toronto, ON), and — strangely enough — the Ontario Insurance Commission.

Doc & Raider is part of the Permanent Collection of the National Archives of Canada.

A Quick Introduction

Ken Popert
Publisher, Xtra Magazine

When *Xtra*, Toronto's gay and lesbian biweekly, conducted a reader survey recently, we discovered two interesting facts about Sean Martin's *Doc & Raider*. First, the cartoon is the best read of the four that we regularly publish. Second — and surprisingly — it's just as popular with lesbians as with gay men.

Sorry, we're gonna have to get back to you. The editors have asked for a "cultural context" for this cartoon...

That stumped us at first because Sean's cartoon is the story of a male couple steeped, for the most part, in the world of leather and chains. But it's also about living together: two people occupying each other's space and time and life, no end in sight.

That may be the key to *Doc & Raider*'s cross-gender popularity: bonding dressed up as bondage, two contracts that paradoxically both free and bind.

So, if you haven't already met, let me introduce you to one of North America's best known gay male couples. This is *Doc & Raider*...

"I don't believe we've me

I'r

Mr. Right."
— one of the world's ten best opening lines, according to <u>Playboy</u>, 1969

The night, they say, was made for love.

We could sit down front with the hard-core enthusiasts, in the middle with the afficionados and critics — or we could just go up in the balcony and neck.

At least *you* never have to worry about putting together an outfit you hope he's going to like...

10

Well, yes, it is a little confusing when they don't sing in
English — so try this: Carmen is my neighbor Frank. Don
Jose therefore is his boyfriend Gary. Escamillo, therefore, is
that hot blond carpenter Frank hired while Gary was in
Québec City. Clearer now?

Look, I just want to let you know that I'm increasing my over-all body strength for peaceful purposes only.

You know, I'm really glad you decided to share the whole white-male guilt-trip thing with me...

... and while we're two-stepping here in Toronto, I wonder if there's a little gay bar somewhere in Montana where the cowboys dress up in tuxedos and dance the tango?

Love
is an exploding cig

GETTING SERIOUS

e willingly smoke.

— *Lynda Barry*

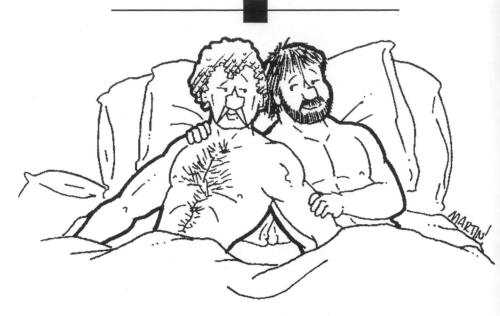

So... was I art?

Same old story. Boy meets girl. Boy loses girl.
Book gets remaindered.

It's not really burned, see...
it's more like cajun chicken flambée...

Well, you're right, of course: it *is* a big cloud, perhaps even enormous — but, Doc, as nice a thing as you've ever said, I don't think it *quite* looks like me getting out of the shower.

Raid, I don't know how to tell you this,
but all this time I've been living a lie.
I'm... I'm... I'm only five-foot-eight...

Sorry, Chris, gotta go. Doc just got to
the fifty-eight minute mark in *Women in Love*.

Hey, if I saw two people having that much fun, I'd probably want to join in too. Of course, I'd do it with my claws *in,* but...

Gee. All I ever get from Randy
is a dumb 'thinking of you' card...

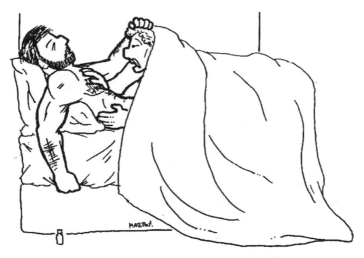

I'll quit when it's no longer a meaningful position.

Brevity is the soul of underwear...

They're writing songs of love, but not for me.

Oh, sure, other couples might have it as good as we do
— but do they have it as often?

Love is blind, but
marriage

MARRIAGE
_____

---■---

a real eye-opener. — *Unknown*

Six hours, five minutes, and forty-three seconds
after the transition from boyfriends to lovers,
Raider suddenly remembers the definition of the word
"commitment."

I'll make this real simple — will you marry me?
Or at the very least, can I marry you?
Or, so we don't seem possessive, could we marry each other?
Or would you rather I just shut up now?

He said
yes!

Wait a minute...
He said *yes*...

A congratulatory card from Paul and John,
a sympathy card from my mother, and a note from
George at Northbound Leather asking
when we're registering our pattern...

No Mendelssohn and no one in a white dress...
I may be a little out of my depth here...

Oh, sure, we've bought rings before, but this is
the first time for this particular piece of anatomy...

Okay, Raid, we'll cancel the wedding if you want.
I'll send the guests home and apologize to the minister,
but you'll have to deal with the caterer's five hundred
stuffed mushrooms.

As long as we both shall live?
Yeah, I think I can handle that...

Great. They take a week off for a "honeymoon",
and you and I get stuck coming up with something funny.
That's it — I'm calling my agent.

The art of *living* more like *wrestling*

COMPROMISE

...an dancing. — *Marcus Aurelius*

Okay! Okay! It's to-*MAH*-to!

Let's hear you *beg* for it, *boy!*

I'll be getting off work by five and getting off the bus by six
so you and I can get off by seven before getting off to
the movies by eight.

Why, yes, it does make you look ten years younger...
but tell me, Doc, are you prepared to shoulder
such an awesome responsibility?

I damn sure hope you remembered cat food.

Andy, I think we're going to need a little more time
to fight over the check.

Proof of a benevolent supreme being?
Richard Locke caught live on tape.

I guess there are some wrinkles
you just can't steam out...

Baby's awake. Your turn.

Well, no, there's no cost-of-living increase this year
because you guys don't draw salaries. You're...
well, how do I put this... you're *pets*.

Oh, yeah, right — like *you* haven't had
a few dress rehearsals for summer...

Practicing homosexual.

Homosexual who missed
practice one too many times
and was subsequently cut
from the team.

It was well after midnight when they decided to go best twenty-six out of fifty, both of knowing that — *eventually* — someone would have to clean out the litter box.

Yeah, but if you *really* loved me... wait a minute. You do, don't you? Well, isn't that just like you: to love me so much I can't hold it against you!

So much for plea-bargaining...

Elliot's finally decided to get himself a new boyfriend
— he just hasn't figured out whose.

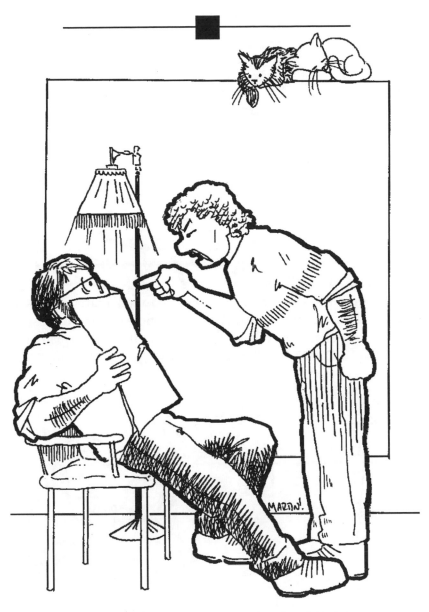

You're insensitive, uncaring, completely oblivious to my needs — and I suggest you not try to deny it, buddy, because I heard all about it on *Oprah*!

Look, I'm really sorry, and it'll never happen again. No. Wait. It just might happen again. All right, there's a strong possibility it'll happen again. Okay, okay, it'll definitely happen again, so why don't you just go ahead and forgive me for that one too?

How fascinatingly convoluted...

Since when does keys-on-the-left mean you get to lead?

I like *men* to behav

like *men*

N E G O T I A T I O N

rong and childish. — *Françoise Sagan*

So... how about a little quarrel before bed?

Whoever said the best things in life are free was sadly mistaken. The best things in life go for about fifty bucks a pound...

So you tell me, buster —
how did *I* get from archetype to anachronism?

It's something on cable called the Discipline Channel,
and I *can't* take my eyes off it...

Yes, he's big and blond and butch and incredibly hot in those little gold lamé shorts... but if you don't waste him, you'll never get to the fourth level of Mylagra and defeat the Evil Warlord of Zignatia.

Excuse me, Mr. Don't-I-Look-Hot, but if a leather bar is holding a fetish night, I for one am dressing for the occasion.

They take 350 years to finally recognize that the earth goes around the sun, and they have the gall to say *we're* unnatural?

Feel like getting a little crazy with the cayenne?

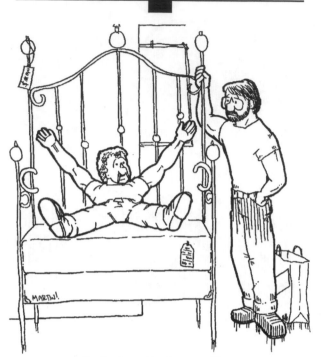

It feels a little small...

Look, if you don't want your ice cream, don't let me stop you.
Just remember there're little fags and dykes elsewhere in the
world who'd appreciate something that's $4.50 a scoop.

Recent polls indicate Doc's domestic performance
rates a two-third approval rating...

Let's see. The airline lost our luggage. The hotel had a fire.
And our return flight was delayed by a surprise blizzard. But
the worst thing about the trip to New York had to be our
finding out that Abba is making a comeback...

I'm here. I'm queer. I'm also late. Get used to it.

Boy! Try to bring a simple pair of handcuffs in
on your carry-on luggage!

Well, yeah, so it's early and we're leaving. Some of us, my
dear Elliot, leave the bar early because we have to, and some
of us leave the bar early because we *have* to.

Well, maybe I was a little rude when the auditor said I wasn't your legal spouse, but did he have to drag the *cats* into it?

Wait a minute... what the hell are you cooking?
This is *The Leather Journal!*

As best as I can tell, from there we went to Badlands,
then to the 501, *then* to Pints...

Dear Bob,

Well, as you may have heard, Doc did
it again — he managed to win the
Toronto Mr. Drummer contest, and
that means a return to the finals.
This time, he said, he was doing it
right, he'd have it all down pat.
After lots of study, he certainly
knew his leather lore...

DOC GOES TO THE INTERNATIONAL MR. DRUMMER CONTEST

Okay, okay, I got it now. Leather pants are better than jeans and chaps. Jeans and chaps are better than chaps and a leather jock, which are better than just jeans, which in turn are better than just a jock, whether cotton or leather, although leather is better, of course — unless you're into a locker room scene, in which case all of this becomes academic. Now, the hanky code, all seventy-two entries, left pocket, then right. Number one: *red..*"

We arrive in San Francisco to a flurry of activity: registration, credentials, regulations...

Okay, let me get *your* set of rule books...

There were costume fittings and rehearsals of the big production number's choreography...

Look, dammit, I'm the fucking director, and I'm telling you this is *too goddam big!* I want to see *flesh* out there — *understand?*

I daresay perhaps some of you gentlemen would feel more comfortable performing Les Sylphides... *However...*

Then came Doc's big night. We were in the fantasy section of the evening, and I was damned if I was doing that "human xylophone" again. Doc thought otherwise, and before long we'd brought our "discussion" onstage, much to our chagrin and — believe it or not — the judges' and audience's delight...)

71

It managed to score him enough points that he wound up one of the finalists... and I gotta tell you, it was quite a sight, seeing those three up there in brotherhood and friendship...

Then came the announcement he'd been waiting for. He'd worked so hard for something that came down to a few simple words: "The International Mr. Drummer for 1993 is..."

He'd won! God only knows how, but he'd won! And even so he handled it with his usual aplomb...

They had this huge production number congratulating the winner...

... followed by the bestowment of prizes. To be honest, I wasn't real sure whether he **actually** <u>needed</u> some of this stuff...

... a lifetime supply of Crisco, a complete set of Rubbermaid, six rolls of Robert Danté wallpaper in the new "Whips Across America" pattern, a portable dungeon-and-sling set, a two-hour session with Mad Marcus, Wrestler for Hire...

From there, it was almost mind-numbing: interviews with the gay and lesbian media...

Would you classify this as an affirmation of personal style or a mere beauty contest whose participants pander to the baser instincts of judges and an audience who would otherwise be serving the needs of the larger lesbian and gay communities? Or, failing that, would you see this as an almost guerrilla-theatre action whose "in your face" methodology is purposely designed to annoy and confuse the more sexually repressed... and why?

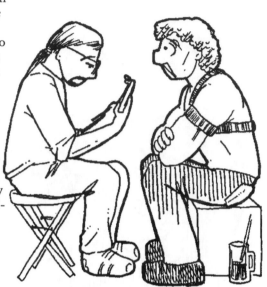

... lots of networking...

... and of course we'd be looking at a five-figure endorsement fee with the country's largest manufacturer of home enemas...

... and a huge party that went on until all hours of the night, at which point I had to get the new Mr. Drummer 1993 home and tucked into bed.

Attention, please, attention — the titleholder has *left* the building... I repeat, the titleholder has *left* the building...

It was indeed an exciting weekend,
filled with excitement and new
friends we'll cherish all our lives,
and, of course, the contest itself.
But he wanted it; he was willing to
work hard to get it — and by God, he
did. I was so happy for Doc. It was
almost like a new era of his life
was about to begin, one bright and
full of promise, one where anything
could happen...

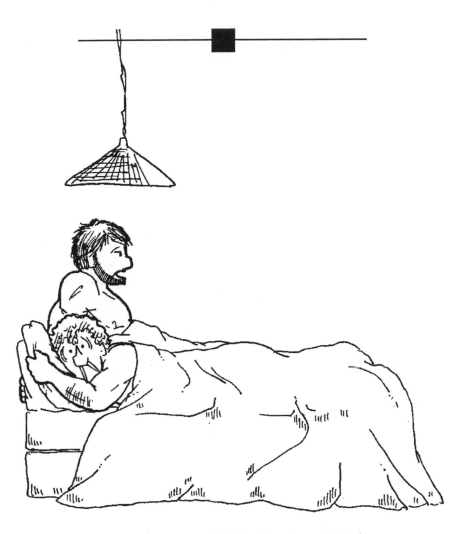

Excuse me, Mister Titleholder, but I think
one of the cats just threw up on your sash...

Regards,
Raider

Lead me not into
temptation

D O M E S T I C I T Y

can find the way myself.
— *Rita Mae Brown*

Fresh catnip?

No, I *don't* think the purchase of a six-foot inflatable dinosaur at a yard sale in Kitchener will have a drastic impact on the overall improvement of the national economy...

Statistically, eight out of ten gay men prefer "tackle" to "touch" football, although exactly why is open to conjecture...

Another neon-based summer wardrobe, I assume.

Now, remember, Flo: if he screams and yells, don't take it personally. It's just *that* time of year again.

D-D-D-DO W-W-W-W-WE HA-HA-HA-HAVE TO B-B-B-BE
SO F-F-FUCK-FUCK-FUCKING MA-MA-MA-MACHO?

It was only a tiny piece of Doc's childhood,
but suddenly it seemed a *very* important piece.

Do you realize we've been together long enough
to try *everything* at Baskin-Robbins?

Forget it, Raid — you're not fooling me.
Under that hard-nosed exterior lies a man
who *always* cries at the ending of Ghost...

Okay. It's not gender specific, exhibits no cultural appropria-
tion, does not appear co-dependent, acknowledges personal
boundaries, is printed on 100% recycled paper with
vegetable-based inks... but, *boy*, it's still one boring
birthday card.

I sometimes think God is running the world by consensus...

COMING TO A TOY STORE MUCH TOO CLOSE TO YOU...

90

I especially like the little metallic things on your boots:
they're just the right touch to warn everyone: "Look out —
it's the Hell's Angel from Oz!"

Red wine, white wine, or do you
just want to meet this head-on?

Would you ever want to know if I'd done something... well,
you know... a little all too human?

Naughty. Nice. I wonder if Santa appreciates
the subtle difference...

I've been watching this thing all day. From the talk shows to the soaps, it's nothing but sex, sex, sex. Is that *all* straight people think about?

Chromium cassettes. CD singles. DATs.
Screw it — I'm going back to my accordion.

Oh, I was just thinking that, statistically, sexual ardor is sup-
posed to disappear after the third year... and how, after five
years with you, all I can think about is ripping your clothes
off. God grief, Doc, where did we go *wrong*?

You know, you may be on to something with this
"strip-chess" stuff...

I can't believe that, here it is, the beginning of summer,
and you're *still* wearing black...

This wasn't shopping. This was...
was... MAGIC!

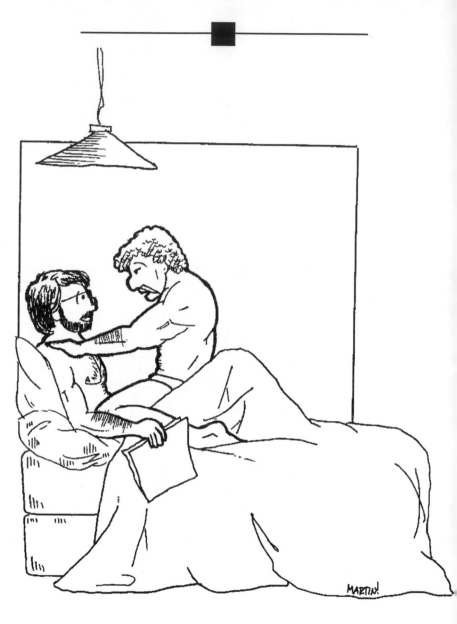

I'm feeling *awfully* phallo-centric...

Oh look, Doc — "contains PCPs". I guess our little social commentator doesn't like the environment much either...

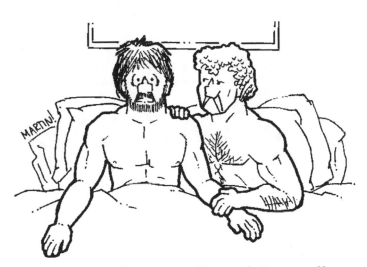

It was awful, Doc! I dreamed there really *was* a Queer Nation!

Some guy in a sheet just asked if I knew Krishna the Beautiful. That's not Elliot's drag name, is it?

Apparently, we haven't used our Visa card this month, and a Mrs. Lundquist from Royal Bank seems quite concerned...

I warned you about trying to skate to Wagner...

You're organic. I like that in a man.

Boy, there's nothing more depressing than a perky blond whose *Golden Girls* re-run gets pre-empted.

Say what you will. I refuse to waste my talents on anything that has to be prepared with more than one ingredient.

104

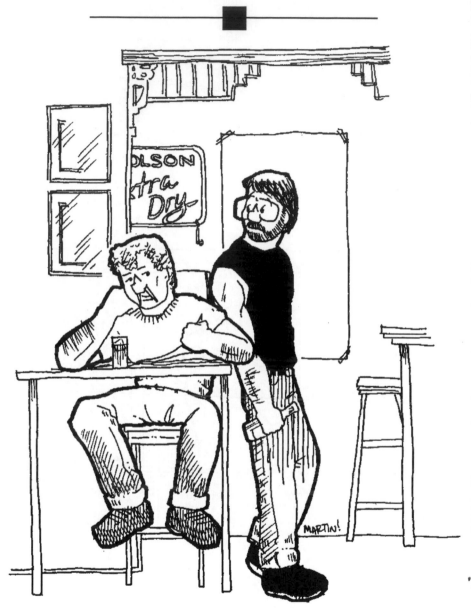

According to the personal ads, guys in their 40s wants guys in their 20s. Guys in their 20s wants guys in their 30s. Guys in their 30s wants guys in their late teens. And guys in their late teens are open to dating anyone — at least *someone* has the right idea...

Don't mind me.. I just thought I'd slip into
something comfortable.

We could spend the afternoon looking for souvenirs —
seashells, native wood carvings, Tom Selleck's stunt double...

What do you mean, "he's writing another show"?

Oh, I'm sure he's feeling better. He just asked for an
International Male catalog and a credit card.

On TV, it's lots of strapping, bare-chested men, their skin glistening from a dive in a country stream, their laughing smiles filled with even, brilliantly white teeth. But here, it's "Pour into saucepan. Heat. Serve when hot."

Well, sure, so maybe it *is* a hard-core S&M porno novel. I just like to think there's something in it for everyone.

Trust me on this. "Mary, Mary, quite contrary, how does your garden grow" will *not* get you the best service.

Isn't it amazing, some of the stuff you can pick up
at these yard sales?

We've got about an hour before the movers get here.
How would you like to pack one more thing?

You know, in a really good bar fight, there's something about seeing a guy's fist only seconds before it smashes into your eye that has an almost existential beauty all its own...

There, there. The summer clothes will
still be there next year, I promise...

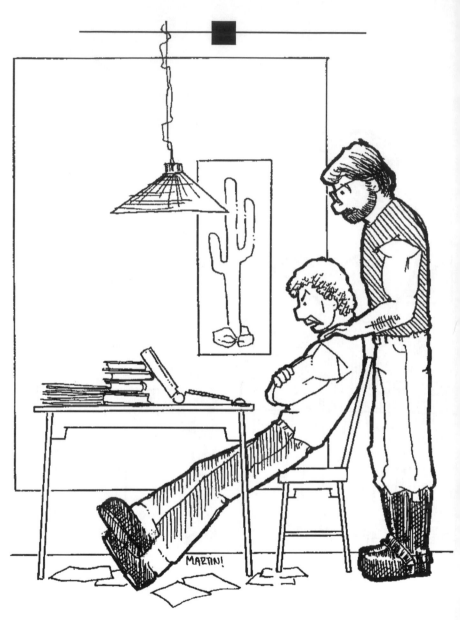

I don't know what the problem is. The characters are all just standing around, staring at each other. It's worse than a leather bar on a Friday night.

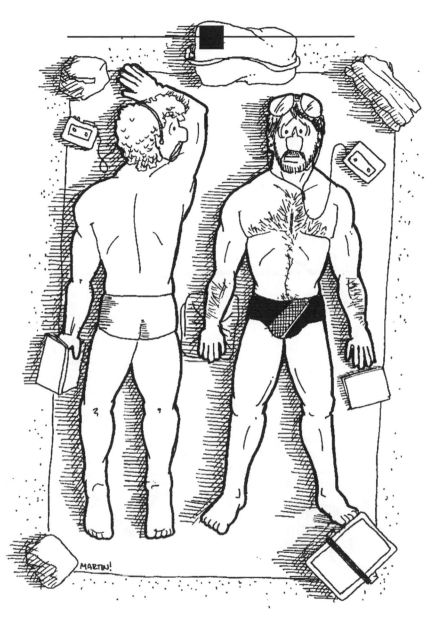

Wait a minute... this isn't our bed. This is the *beach!* We're wearing *lycra* — and — and listening to *dance music! Doc! Quick! Wake up!* We've been kidnapped into a *phone sex ad!*

I'm sorry, Doc. I guess I was just thinking, gee, what a bum deal Tom Selleck was getting in the tabloids, and it made me so darn mad, I just sorta lost control.

You *do* pick the *damnedest* times to express your
appreciation of the artistic value of police uniforms!

Guess which little piggy went to market
and maxed out all our credit cards?

What stunt double?

Have I told you how much,
in purely visual terms, I love you?

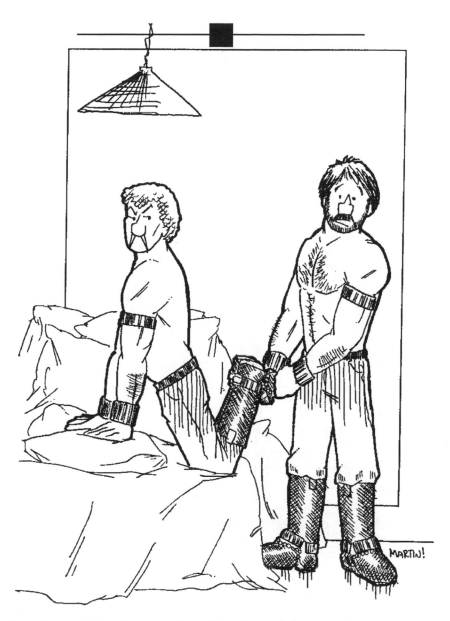

Leather and denim are all well and good, but nothing ruins a
scene faster than a tangled pair of boot chains...

Oh, I know where all the time went —
I just didn't think it would all come home quite so early.

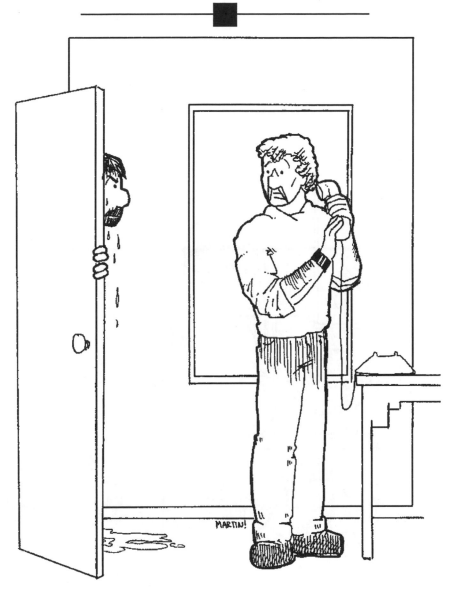

It's Gloria Gaynor.
Did she survive?

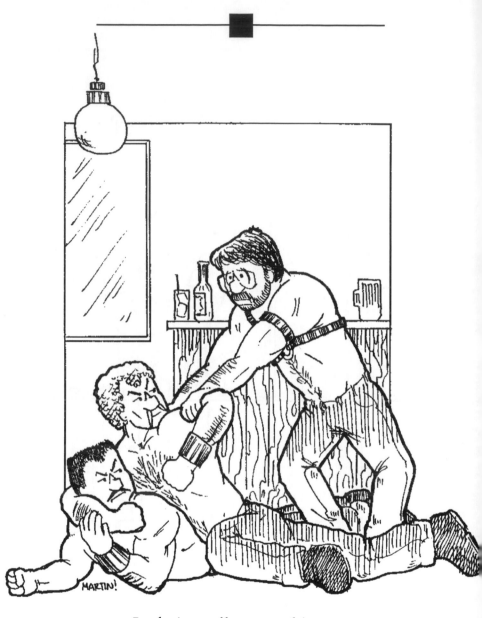

Look, just tell me one thing —
this guy, he doesn't *mean* anything to you, does he?

You know, this is almost like something out of "The
Fisherman and His Wife", except of course we're both guys,
and I kinda doubt there're any magic flounders in Lake
Nippissing...

Okay, Raid, if you wanna play that way: biting, slapping, and punching are all fair game — but rip my sixty-dollar Calvin Kleins, and your ass is *mine...*

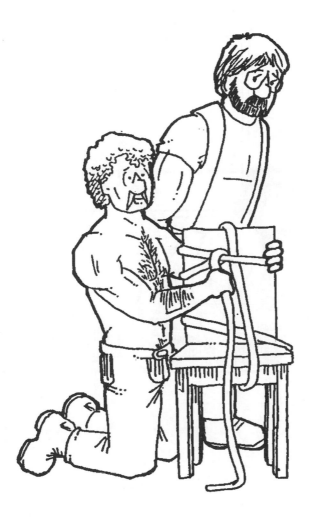

Oh, nothing. Just having a little fun with my air-slave.

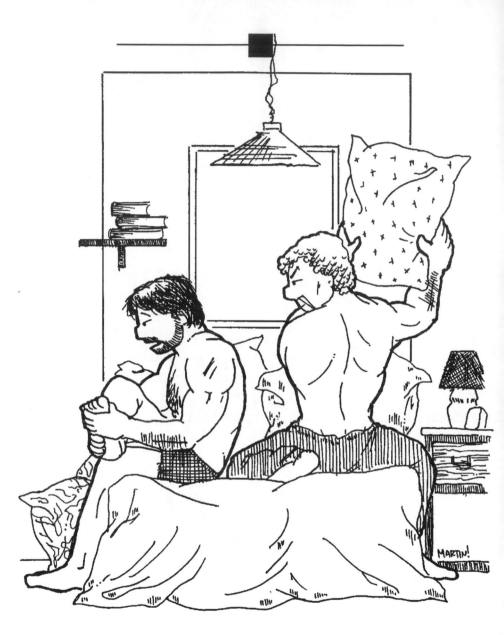

I suppose you want me to believe
you're really angry and not just role-playing?

We were both really old and fat, and we couldn't go to the gym anymore or fit into our leather or even have sex, but after all those years you still knew how to annoy the hell out of me... and dammit, Raid, it was *wonderful*...

"There is no answer. Ther[e]
never has been an answe[r]

CRISIS

That's the answer."

— Gertrude Stein

I was so positive I was negative. Now I find out I'm positive.
All right. I can't be *negative* about this; I have to stay
positive... as if there's any choice...

It's moments like this, whenever I come in for these damn tests, that I find myself wondering: Why are we born? Why do I love you so much? Why the hell did we paint the bedroom that God-awful colour?

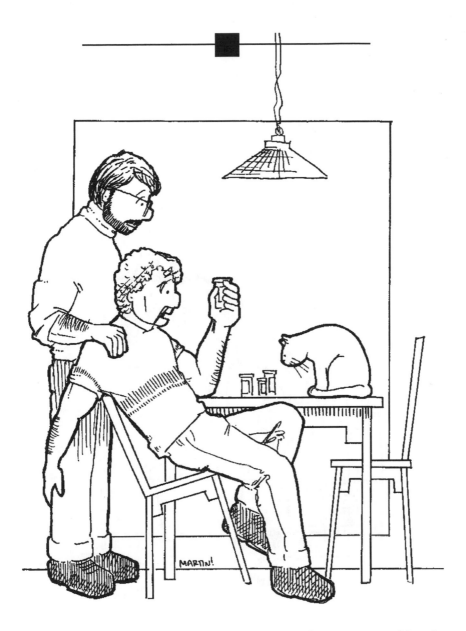

The white ones help my immunal system but raise my blood pressure. The red ones lower my blood pressure but screw up my stomach. The green ones help my stomach but fuck with my immunal system. And these yellow ones simply ensure an attractive colour combination.

Elliot, can you come over, like right now?
Doc's left me...

The note doesn't say much, El, just that he's decided to visit his family. But he doesn't... oh, God... I think I know where he is.

I sorta figured I'd find you here.
You planning on staying with your folks for a while?

They had thirty years together before Dad died.
With my HIV, we'll be lucky to make it to a decade.
Doesn't it make you feel like we're being shortchanged a bit?

Every morning, I wake up and think, we have to cram our thirty years together into one decade. We have to live our relationship in constant fast forward. I want you to *honestly* tell me you can live with that, because sometimes I feel I can't...

All right. If you don't want me to take care of you when you
fall ill — if you want to leave me — fine. Go ahead.
But before you go, let me show you something first...

When you were diagnosed, I bought this so, no matter what, we'd always be together. It's just around the way from your folks. You're on the left, 'cause that's where you always sleep...

Look, you talk it over with your folks and then let me know what you want. I'm heading home to start dinner. Remember, it's your turn to wash up...

Okay, since you're gonna wash up, I'll dry...
See? I even brought a handkerchief...

A Few Final Thoughts

Marcus-Jay Wonacott
Managing Editor, Drummer Magazine
Desmodus, Inc

It's hard for me to think of Doc and Raider as line-drawn characters and not my best friends who live around the corner. My first impression when we met was "How cute: a gay leather couple." However, as familiarity grows, so does my sense of being connected with them. Raider's temper is just like mine; I admire his ability to express it — he wears a black eye well! I look up to Doc in admiration for his keen fashion sense and the inevitable ability to accessorize. I'm sure our pets know each other, conferring regularly on the subject of night surveillance under the sheets!

It isn't every day that characters in a strip reveal the hardships to which many of us are exposed. I am honoured to share with Doc and Raider our day-to-day struggle living with HIV. Life does, indeed, go on. The inspiration comes from the humour we find in the simplest notions. Doc and Raider have found that rare ability to bring out joy in us all and to pull up our bootstraps for us as we trudge through another day.

I look forward to the next dinner party, when I can join in the battle-royale for the last crudité.

About the Artist

Sean Martin was born in the hamlet of _____
in _____, just south of the _____ border.
Now a resident the charming city of _____,
_____ (near the sleepy little festival village of
_____), his cartoons are seen in a staggering ____
publications around the world. He stands ____ feet, ____
inches, has _____ hair, and weighs _____ pounds
buck-ass naked.

(photo: Forge Studios)